CONSUMER MATHEMATICS OCCUPATIONAL DIAGRAMS

W9-AWV-445

CONTENTS

Author:	**Thomas W. Hazard, Ph.D.**
Editor-in-Chief:	Richard W. Wheeler, M.A.Ed.
Editor:	Stephany L. Sykes
Consulting Editor:	Robert L. Zenor, M.A., M.S.
Illustrator:	Thomas R. Rush

AOP

804 N. 2nd Ave. E., Rock Rapids, IA 51246-1759
© MCMLXXIX by Alpha Omega Publications, Inc. All rights reserved.
LIFEPAC is a registered trademark of Alpha Omega Publications, Inc.

OCCUPATIONAL DIAGRAMS

If you were asked what the following occupations had in common—land surveyor, architect, design engineer, clothes designer, cartographer, machinist, electrician, navigator, and draftsman—you would probably come up with several answers that would apply to most of these occupations. However, you would probably have a hard time finding a single common characteristic.

The answer is that all these occupations require the ability to read and interpret a diagram. The land surveyor should be able to read a topographical map; the architect, a blueprint; the design engineer, an engineering drawing; the clothes designer, a pattern; the cartographer, a map; the machinist, a shop drawing; the electrician, a wiring diagram; the navigator, an oceanographic or aerial map; and the draftsman, a mechanical drawing.

This LIFEPAC will enable you to understand and interpret the most common diagrams used in these occupations. The LIFEPAC will also help you understand the symbols, the purpose, and the techniques for preparation in these occupations.

OBJECTIVES

Read these objectives. The objectives tell you what you will be able to do when you have successfully completed this LIFEPAC.

When you have finished this LIFEPAC, you should be able

1. To calculate and employ fractions, ratios, and proportions used in scaled diagrams;

2. To convert the dimensions of an object to scale for representation in various occupational diagrams;

3. To read a map using the grid coordinate system;

4. To interpret contour lines used on a map;

5. To interpret and show critical dimensions employed with occupational diagrams;

6. To draw angles of given sizes and verify their magnitudes;

7. To construct various polygons and calculate their critical dimensions;

8. To inscribe regular polygons in circles;

9. To answer questions about scale diagrams used in house plans;

10. To answer questions about floor plans including placement of furnishings; and

11. To calculate costs associated with furnishing a house.

Survey the LIFEPAC. Ask yourself some questions about this study. Write your questions here.

_____

_____

_____

_____

_____

_____

_____

I. SCALE DRAWINGS

OBJECTIVES

1. To calculate and employ fractions, ratios, and proportions used in scaled diagrams.
2. To convert the dimensions of an object to scale for representation in various occupational diagrams.
3. To read a map using the grid coordinate system.
4. To interpret contour lines used on a map.
5. To interpret and show critical dimensions employed with occupational diagrams.

So that diagrams used in various occupations may be accurate representations of the objects' dimensions and orientation, the principles of scale drawing need to be learned and applied. A review of some of the basic mathematical skills needed will be helpful.

REVIEWING MATHEMATICAL OPERATIONS

Before working with scale drawings, a few mathematical operations need to be reviewed since they are basic to converting dimensions to different scales. The first operation has to do with fractions, and the second operation has to do with ratios and proportions.

A fraction is a number that is not a whole number. The number $\frac{5}{8}$ is a fraction. On the other hand, $\frac{4}{2}$ may be written in fractional form, but since it reduces to a whole number, 2, it is not a fraction. In the fraction $\frac{5}{8}$, the numeral below the line is the denominator, and the numeral above the line is the numerator. The denominator, or 8 in this case, tells us into how many parts the unit is divided. The numerator, 5 in this case, indicates how many of these parts are taken. Thus, if we were using a ruler, and each eighth were equivalent to $\frac{1}{8}$ inch, $\frac{5}{8}$ would be equivalent to $\frac{5}{8}$ inch.

A fraction is normally reduced to its lowest terms. A fraction is reduced when the numerator and the denominator have no common factor other than 1.

Model: Reduce $\frac{10}{15}$.

Since the common factor or divisor of both numerals is 5, we divide both the numerator and the denominator by 5.

$$\frac{10}{15} = \frac{\frac{10}{5}}{\frac{15}{5}} = \frac{2}{3}$$

When you add or subtract fractions, change all the denominators into what is called the lowest common denominator. Finding the lowest common denominator

is finding the smallest (lowest) number
into which all the denominators can be
divided evenly without a remainder.

Model: Find the lowest common denominator of
the fractions $\frac{1}{4}$, $\frac{1}{12}$, and $\frac{1}{6}$ and add these
fractions.

The lowest common denominator is 12.
The equivalent of $\frac{1}{4}$ is $\frac{3}{12}$, $\frac{1}{12}$ does not
have to be converted, and the equivalent
of $\frac{1}{6}$ is $\frac{2}{12}$. Adding, $\frac{3}{12} + \frac{1}{12} + \frac{2}{12} = \frac{6}{12}$.
Reducing, $\frac{6}{12} = \frac{1}{2}$.

A method of stating the relationship of one number to another number is
the calculation of a *ratio*. A ratio
includes two numbers. If a field has
a length of 100 yards and a width of
25 yards, the ratio of the length to
the width is expressed as $\frac{100}{25}$ or 100:25.
Both expressions have the same meaning.
As with fractions, ratios are reduced
to lowest terms. The ratio $\frac{100}{25}$, therefore,
should be reduced to $\frac{4}{1}$, or 4:1.
We could also have found the ratio of
the width to the length: $\frac{25}{100}$ or 25:100.
Reducing, we obtain the ratio of the
width to the length as $\frac{1}{4}$, or 1:4

Model: A blueprint is drawn in the ratio of $\frac{1}{2}$ inch
to 1 foot. Each $\frac{1}{2}$ inch represents 1 foot of
the actual object being represented. Converting 1 foot into 12 inches, the ratio is
$\frac{1}{2}$:12. Multiplying by 2, the ratio $\frac{1}{2}$:12
becomes 1:24. Suppose an object depicted in
the blueprint actually measures 6 feet in
length. How long will it appear in the
blueprint?

Since the ratio is 1:24, and 6 feet convert
to 72 inches, then $\frac{72}{24} = 3$, and 3 x 1 = 3 inches
on the blueprint.

A *proportion* is a statement of equality
between ratios. Therefore, 3:4 = 6:8 is
a proportion. Another way of stating this
relationship is "three is to four as six is
to eight." A different method of writing
the proportional form is 3:4::6:8. In this
method the double colon in the middle is
the same as the equal sign. The fractional
of the proportion is expressed as $\frac{3}{4} = \frac{6}{8}$.

In any proportion the first and last
terms are called the *extremes*. The second
and third terms are called the *means*. If
any three of the four numbers are known,
then the fourth number can be determined,
because the product of the means equals
the product of the extremes.

Model: What is *m* in the proportion 2:5 = *m*:10?
Using the relationship of extremes and
means, the product of the extremes,
2 x 10, equals the product of the means,
5 x *m*. Solving for *m*, we obtain
$m = \frac{2 \times 10}{5} = 4$.

Solve the following problems.

1.1   Reduce $\frac{14}{21}$.   _____

1.2   Add $\frac{2}{3}$, $\frac{5}{6}$, and $\frac{10}{18}$.   _____

1.3   A box measures 6" in length and
4" in width. What is the ratio   _____
of its length to its width?

1.4   Given: 6:4::*C*:8
Find *C*.   _____

Match these items.

1.5   ____ fraction

1.6   ____ reduced to lowest terms

1.7   ____ includes two numbers

1.8   ____ statement of equality
between ratios

1.9   ____ first and last terms

a. numerator and denominator
have no common factor
other than 1

b. not a whole number

c. extremes

d. proportion

e. ratio

f. greatest common multiple

The following definition of a scale will help you as you read this section.

DEFINITION

A *scale* is the size of a plan, a map, a drawing, or a model compared with what it represents.

The scale varies with the function of the drawing being employed. For example, an architect might use a scale of $\frac{1}{4}$ inch = 1 foot, and a *cartographer* (a person who makes maps) might use a scale of 1 inch = 50 miles.

The use of an appropriate scale permits the drawer to convert the actual dimensions of an object to a scale convenient to the size of the drawing he wishes to make without distortion.

Model 1: A house measures 60 feet in length and 25 feet in width. If a scale of $\frac{1}{4}$ inch = 1 foot is used, what are the dimensions of a scale drawing of the house?

Since $\frac{1}{4}$ inch = 1 foot, multiplying by 4, 1 inch = 4 feet. Therefore, $\frac{60}{4}$ = 15 inches and $\frac{25}{4}$ = $6\frac{1}{4}$ inches. The house on the scale drawing will measure 15 inches in length and $6\frac{1}{4}$ in width.

Model 2: A box constructed in a metal shop measures 16" long, 12" wide, and 4" deep. The shop foreman instructs you to make a scale drawing of the box. What scale will you use, and what will the dimensions of the box be?

To select an appropriate scale, you should consider convenience not only to yourself in terms of drawing a scalar representations, but also to whoever is going to read the drawing. If you choose a scale of $\frac{1}{4}"$ = 1", the box length will be $\frac{16}{4}$ = 4"; the box width will be $\frac{12}{4}$ = 3"; and the box depth will be $\frac{4}{4}$ = 1".

These measurements are satisfactory because they are small enough to fit on a sheet of paper, and yet large enough to give the necessary detail of the box.

Since maps generally cover large distances and enclose large areas (states, cities, or even countries), scales on maps involve large number conversion. Scales of 1 inch = 1,000 feet, 1 inch = 5 miles, or 1 inch = 100 miles are more appropriate for large distances and areas than scales of 1 inch = 1 foot or 1 inch = 1 mile would be.

Model 1: You are looking at a city map. You see in the map's legend that 1" = 1,000'. If the city limits are included in a map distance measuring 36" wide (west-east direction) and 24" high (south-north direction), how many miles, approximately, do the city limits actually cover?

Since 1" = 1,000', 36" = 36,000'; but 5,280 feet = 1 mile. Therefore, dividing 36,000 by 5,280, we obtain 6.8 miles as the approximate distance from west to east. Dividing 24,000 by 5,280, we obtain 4.5 miles as the approximate distance from south to north.

Model 2: You intend to drive from Jones City to Jackson Heights. On the road map you have you measure the map distance to be about $3\frac{1}{2}$ inches. Looking at the map scale, you find that 1 inch = 5 miles. How many miles is Jones City from Jackson Heights?

1 inch:5 miles = 3.5 inches:m miles
$5 \times 3.5 = m$
17.5 or $17\frac{1}{2} = m$

The distance from Jones City to Jackson Heights is $17\frac{1}{2}$ miles.

Solve the following problems.

1.10   Given a map scale of 1 inch = 50
        miles, find the map distance between
        two cities 75 miles apart.

        _____

1.11   Given the map scale of 1 inch =
        10 km, find the distance between
        two mountains that measure 1¼ in.
        apart on the map.

        _____

1.12   The scale of a blueprint is ¼" =
        1'. If a house has 1 bedroom
        measuring 10'6" by 11', a living
        room measuring 25' by 18'8", a
        kitchen measuring 13'6" by 8', and
        a dining room measuring 12' x 10',
        what are the respective scale
        dimensions of the

        a. bedroom   _____

        b. living room   _____

        c. kitchen, and   _____

        d. dining room?   _____

READING MAPS

    So far we have discussed scale in one
form, as it is used in maps. However, map
scales may be represented in other forms.
    A figure such as 1:50,000 is called a
representative fraction. This figure means
that for every unit on a certain map, 50,000
of these same units are on the ground. The
figure also means that approximately 1¼ inches
equal one mile.

    Model: Given a map scale of 1:50,000, what is
              the ground distance expressed in miles
              between two towns that are 6" apart on
              the given map?

$$1:50,000 = 6:d$$
$$1d = 300,000$$

(Remember, product of extremes = product of means.) $\dfrac{300,000}{5,280 \times 12} = \dfrac{300,000}{63,360}$

Therefore, ground distance = 4.7 miles.

Scales may also be represented by a graphic line scale such as the following one.

```
  0      8      16 miles
```

In this scale 1 inch = 16 miles. The alternate black and white segments are $\frac{1}{4}$ inch long and, hence, are equivalent to 4 miles each.

On maps a system of evenly spaced lines forming a lattice is used as an aid to locate objects. This system is referred to as a *grid*. From a single point of reference in the National Grid System, all maps are divided into a series of grids based on their distance from this common center.

Grid lines are at kilometer intervals and are numbered according to the following procedure.

PROCEDURE

A *map grid system* is composed of vertical lines called *East-ings* that are numbered in the top and bottom margins of the map, and of horizontal lines called *Northings* that are numbered at the sides of the map. These numbers are always quoted in pairs and are used to designate any single kilo-meter square on the map. For any square the number of the line that corresponds to its West boundary is quoted first, and the number that corresponds to the lower boundary of the square is quoted second.

Model: Given the following grid, how will
           you designate square A?

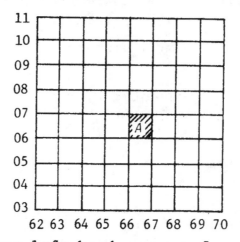

The lower left-hand corner of square A
is read along the Eastings and Northings
margins, reading the Eastings number first.
The Eastings number is 66.   The Northings
number is 06.   Therefore, square A is
designated by 6606 on the map.

This particular square can be further
divided into hundred meter squares
permitting you to designate a particular
terrain feature (such as a church) by
a six-digit grid reference number.

For ease of viewing this latter technique,
square A has been expanded and a symbol
placed within the square representing
a church.

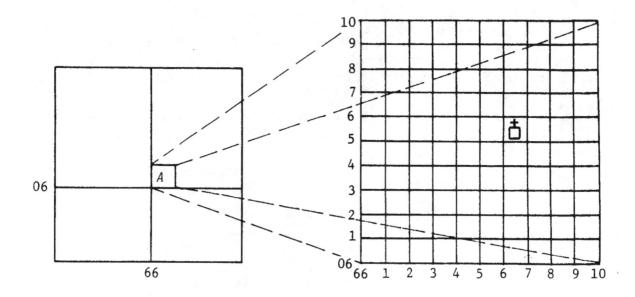

Each row in expanded square *A* represents
10,000 square meters. Since there are 10
sections in each direction the whole square has
1,000,000 square meters, which is one square
kilometer.

Again, we read this square *A* as we did
before, but we add to each previous number
a third number that stands for the $\frac{1}{10}$ distance
in an Easting direction and a Northing
direction respectively. Thus, for the church
depicted, its grid designation in its lower
left-hand corner is 6 across and 5 up.
The whole designation is 660665.

One other important map feature that is
of special interest to the surveyor is the
contour line. Contour lines are used on
topographical maps to indicate places of
equal height above sea level. Contour
lines are usually light brown in color,
are broken at intervals by numbers corresponding to their height in feet, and are
usually in hundred-foot intervals.
The following figure will help you
visualize how a section of terrain
actually appears according to its contour
lines on the map.

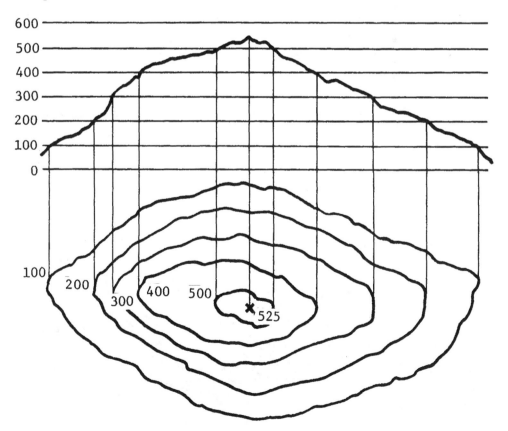

Notice how the left slope is much steeper than the more gently sloping ridge line to the right. Notice also how these slopes are depicted in more closely packed contour lines on the left side and in wider-spaced contours on the right side.

■■■■ Perform the following activities.

1.13 Designate the grid reference number for the mine shown.

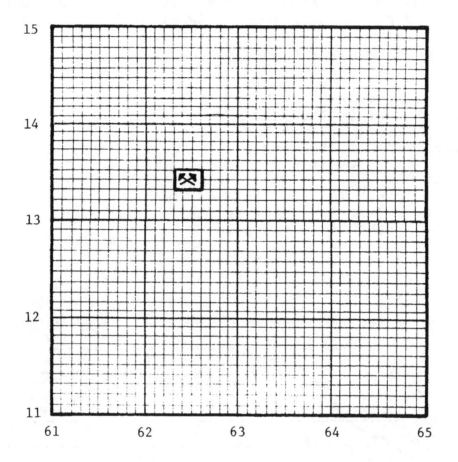

_____

1.14 Read the elevation for the peak shown.

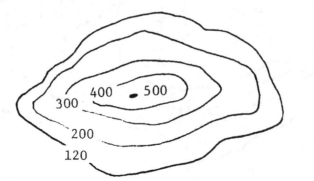

_____

■■■ Complete the following sentences.

1.15 A series of light brown lines drawn at intervals of 50 feet to designate their respective heights above sea level are called _____.

1.16 When reading a grid reference number corresponding to a grid on a map, you read the pair of numbers corresponding to the _____ corner of the square.

1.17 Contour lines fairly evenly spaced and relatively far apart denote a more _____ slope than contour lines unevenly spaced and relatively close together.

1.18 One square kilometer grids are divided into _____ to locate objects to the nearest 100 meters.

Teacher check _____
            Initial   Date

READING SCALE DRAWINGS

On scale drawings objects are shown by *plane figures* that show key sizes in two dimensions and by *modified plane figures* that represent solids with key sizes in three dimensions. Both types of drawings are drawn to some convenient scale.

Figure 1 represents the top view of an office building and is shown with its scale dimensions.

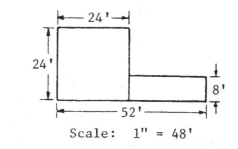

Scale: 1" = 48'

Figure 1: Top View of Office Building

Note the following features of this view:
(1) Key dimensions are shown by arrows indicating
the distances being measured and their orientation,
with numbers corresponding to actual distances
drawn to the appropriate scale. (2) Not all
dimensions are shown, just those needed to
determine the critical dimensions. For example,
you do not need to show that the 52' side is
made up of two sections, one 24' in length and
the other one 28' in length--the difference
between 52' and 24'. Where a small space
appears on the scale drawing, such as at the
8-foot end, the number is placed in the
interval and the arrows are positioned to show
the distance as illustrated.

A front view of this office building looks
like Figure 2a and a back view looks like
Figure 2b. Note that scale dimensions have been
placed on only one figure.

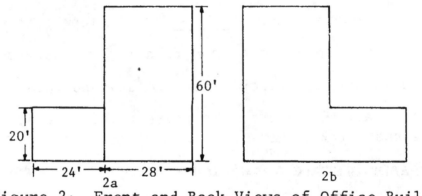

Figure 2: Front and Back Views of Office Building

Another view is an end view. For this
building the end view from the left is shown
in Figure 3L. The end view from the
right is shown in Figure 3R.

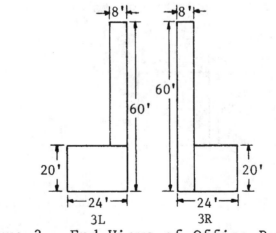

Figure 3: End Views of Office Building

Once again, note that a minimum
number of dimensions are shown, and that
they are consistent with the designated
key distances and orientation.

Finally, although this drawing is not
essential to understand the configuration
of the building, a perspective view is
shown in Figure 4.

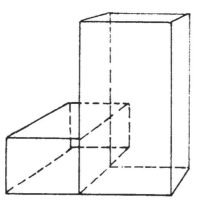

Figure 4:   Perspective View of Office Building

Note that the perspective view may not
have the dimensions indicated. If the
perspective view were critical to under-
standing the object's layout, then
dimensions might be shown for unusual
features. However, the preceding perspective
gives a sense of a three-dimensional solid
figure.

Sometimes we need to know the area
and the perimeter of specific geometric
figures, such as a rectangular field or
an irregularly shaped house lot.

For the perimeter we measure the
border of the field. For the area we
measure the space enclosed within the
field.

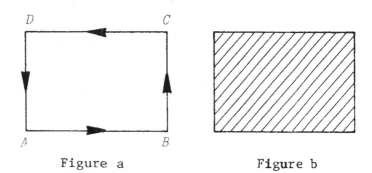

Figure a   Figure b

Both of the rectangles shown represent the same field. To find the perimeter, imagine that you start walking from corner A, and count the paces as you move counter-clockwise completely around the field. The perimeter is the number of paces stepped off from corner A to corner B, plus the number of paces from corner B to corner C, plus the number of paces from corner C to corner D, plus the number of paces from corner D and back to the starting point at corner A. If your paces were the same and they measured $2\frac{1}{2}$ feet per stride, you can convert the total paces to feet by multiplying the sum of paces by 2.5 feet.

Model: Suppose you walk 100 paces each from corner A to corner B and from corner C to corner D, and 30 paces each from corner B to corner C and from corner D to corner A. The perimeter will be

$$P = 100 + 30 + 100 + 30 = 260 \text{ paces}$$
$$\text{or } P = 260(2.5') \qquad\qquad = 650'.$$

For the area computation look at Figure b. The area is shown by shading. We can find the area by counting the number of square blocks measuring 1 inch by 1 inch. The rectangle shown has 21 blocks altogether. Since the blocks are 1 square inch each, the area = 21 square inches. The same result can be obtained by counting the blocks along the long side, 7, and multiplying that number by the number of blocks along the short side, 3.

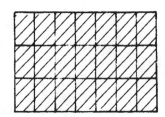

Figure b

$$A = (7)(3) = 21 \text{ sq. inches, or } 21 \text{ in.}^2$$

Model: Find the area of a field in the shape of a rectangle that measures 90' on the long side and 25' on the short side.

$$A = (90')(25') = 2,250 \text{ ft.}^2$$

Suppose our lot is shaped like the figure shown.

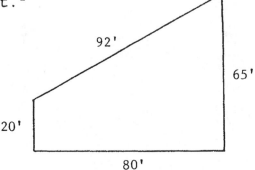

To find the perimeter, add all of the
sides: $P = 65' + 80' + 20' + 92'$. Therefore,
the perimeter is equal to 257'.

To compute the area, we have a different
situation. The easiest procedure is to divide
the area into a system of regular geometric
figures for which we have area formulas.
Then, we sum all those subareas to arrive
at the total area.

For example, we can divide this lot
as shown.

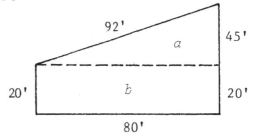

By drawing a line parallel to the 80-foot
side, we have formed a right triangle, a, and
a rectangle, b.

Note that the right side of the lot is now
divided into a 20-foot side and a 45-foot side.

The area of the rectangle is 20 ft. times
80 ft., or 1,600 square feet (or ft.^{2}). The
area of the right triangle is $\frac{1}{2}$ times the base
times the altitude. The dotted line is
perpendicular to the 45-foot line; therefore,
it is the altitude of the triangle. Its
length is 80 feet. The base is 45 feet, as
we already indicated. Therefore, the area of
the triangle = $\frac{1}{2}$ x 80 ft. x 45 ft., or 1,800 ft.^{2}
Hence, the area of the lot equals the sum of
1,600 ft.^{2} and 1,800 ft.^{2}, or 3,400 ft.^{2}

Match the correct items.

1.19 _____ arrows on scale drawing

1.20 _____ top, side, and end views

1.21 _____ perspective view

1.22 _____ scale distance

a. representation of
   a two-dimensional
   object

b. distance measured
   on drawing

c. contain distance
   number and show
   orientation

d. normal drawings of an
   object

e. representation of a
   three-dimensional
   object

█████ Solve these problems.

1.23 The sides of a right triangle are
10", 6", and 8". Find the perimeter.

_____

1.24 For the triangle in Problem 1.23,
find the area.

_____

1.25 Compute the area of the following
rectangle.

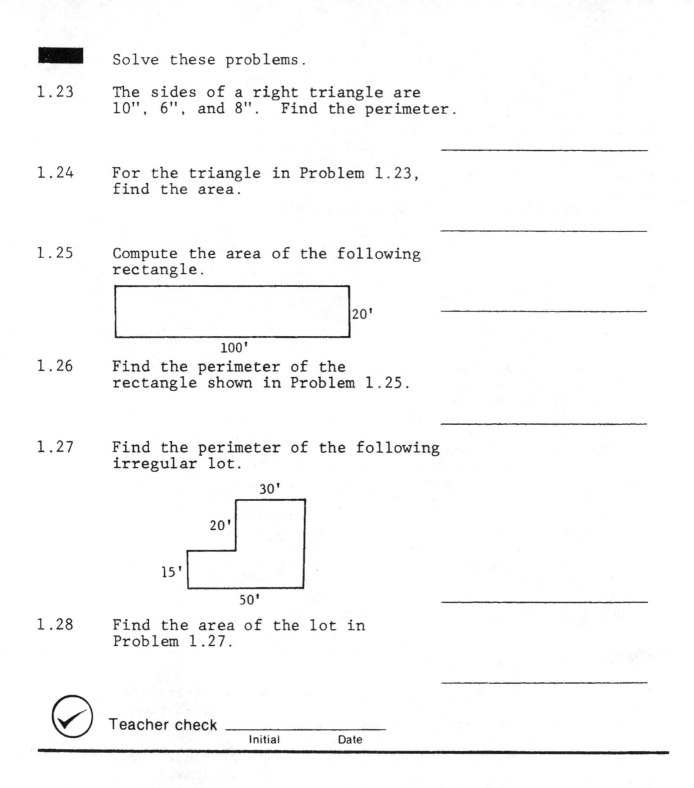

20'

_____

100'

1.26 Find the perimeter of the
rectangle shown in Problem 1.25.

_____

1.27 Find the perimeter of the following
irregular lot.

30'

20'

15'

50'

_____

1.28 Find the area of the lot in
Problem 1.27.

_____

 Teacher check _____
Initial   Date

REVIEW Review the material in this section in preparation for the Self Test. The Self
Test will check your mastery of this particular section. The items missed on this
Self Test will indicate specific areas where restudy is needed for mastery.

SELF TEST 1

Write the letter of the correct item in the blank (each answer, 2 points).

1.01   A scale is a diagram or ruler marked off conveniently

to represent proportionally larger or smaller _____.

a. angles   c. perpendiculars

b. dimensions   d. inches

1.02   When adding or subtracting fractions change all the

_____ to the lowest common denominator.

a. denominators   c. reciprocals

b. numerators   d. numerals

1.03   Contour lines are used on topographical maps to in-

dicate places of _____ above sea level.

a. variable height   c. equal height

b. slope height   d. great distances

Write *true* or *false* (each answer, 2 points).

1.04   _____   When you read a grid square, you read the pair
of numerals corresponding to the lower left-
hand corner.

1.05   _____   A map-grid system is composed of vertical lines
called Westings and horizontal lines called
Northings.

1.06   _____   A six-digit grid reference number locates an
object on a map down to and including a square
of 100 meters on a side.

Complete these activities (each problem, 4 points).

1.07   Draw the specified views of the following object.

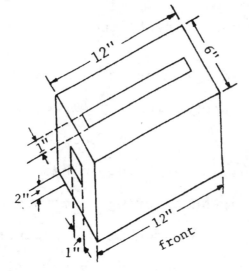

    a. top view   b. front view   c. end view

1.08   Find the dimensions indicated for the following figure.

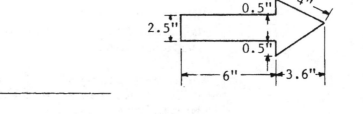

    a. Perimeter _____

    b. Area   _____

Solve the following problems (each answer, 3 points).

1.09   Reduce the fraction $\frac{15}{45}$.   _____

1.010   Find C in the proportion $14:56::42:C$.

                                                      _____

1.011   The radii of two circles are 15" and 75"
         respectively. What is the ratio of the
         radius of the smaller circle to the
         radius of the larger circle?

         _____

1.012   The scale of a blueprint is $\frac{1}{4}$ in. =
         1 ft. If an object to be drawn
         actually measures 14 feet long, 6
         feet wide, and 2 feet deep, what are
         its scale dimensions?

                                              a. _____

                                              b. _____

                                              c. _____

1.013   A certain map scale is 1:100,000.
         If two towns are 5" apart on the map,
         what is the actual distance between
         these two towns to the nearest tenth
         of a mile?

         _____

1.014   Add $\frac{1}{25}$, $\frac{4}{50}$, $\frac{8}{100}$, and $\frac{3}{25}$.   _____

Perform the following task (correct diagram, 4 points).

1.015   For the terrain feature shown, sketch a
         side view representing how the feature will
         appear.

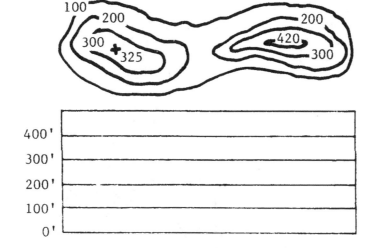

Score   _____
Teacher check _____
                    Initial   Date

II. INFORMAL GEOMETRY

OBJECTIVES

6. To draw angles of given sizes and verify their magnitudes.
7. To construct various polygons and calculate their critical dimensions.
8. To inscribe regular polygons in circles.

Geometric figures and relationships are extremely important to the draftsman or the diagrammer. The ability to interpret and to diagram hexagonal and octagonal polygons is necessary for reading shop drawings since most nuts used in machine parts are in one of the two shapes.

ANGLES

Angles are basic to geometric figures. The three kinds of angles are acute angles, right angles, and obtuse angles. Acute angles are angles that are less than 90°. Right angles are angles that are equal to 90°. Obtuse angles are angles that are greater than 90°.

Draftsmen and architects often use a protractor to draw and measure angles. The following figure represents a standard protractor. You will note that it is in the form of a semicircle marked off in a counterclockwise direction (right to left) from 0 to 180 on the outside row of numbers. It is marked off in a clockwise direction (left to right) from 0 to 180 on the inside row of numbers.

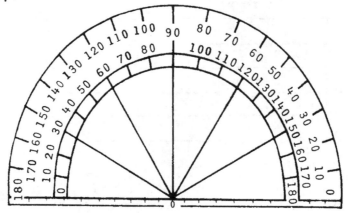

Figure 1: Protractor

Note also that, at the center of the base line, the protractor has an index point labeled 0.

When an angle of given magnitude (of a certain number of degrees) is to be drawn, line up the protractor so that the base line coincides with, or is directly on, an arbitrary line drawn on paper. Then using the 0-index point as a reference point, move along the outside row of numbers at the right until you reach the number corresponding to the size, or magnitude, of the angle to be drawn.

Assume the angle desired is 40°. At the place marked 40 on the protractor (remember: use the outside row only), make a pencil dot. Draw a straight line connecting the two points. The angle formed by the base line on the diagram and the new line is 40° (see the following figure for clarification).

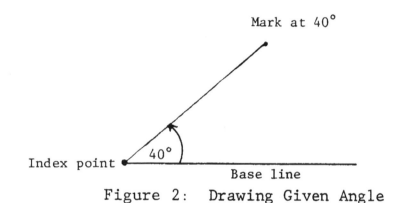

Mark at 40°

40°

Index point

Base line

Figure 2: Drawing Given Angle

The angle is labeled with "40°" as shown to indicate to anyone who reads the diagram that the angle has a magnitude of 40°.

Proceeding in the same manner, an angle greater than 90° but less than, or equal to, 180° can be drawn.

Model: Draw an angle of 130°.

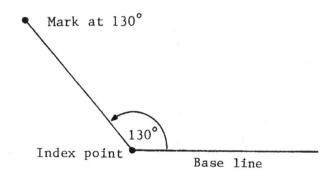

Mark at 130°

130°

Index point

Base line

For angles greater than 180° the protractor is placed along the base line, but inverted so that the semicircle points down. For a reading between 180° and 360°, first determine how many degrees more than 180° the angle has and locate the angle on the protractor that corresponds with that amount.

Model: You wish to draw an angle of 240°. How do you proceed?

First, draw a base line with a straightedge. Now draw a dot for the index point in the middle of the line. Invert the protractor so that it points down. Since 240° is 60° more than 180°, make a mark at 60° on your paper. Now draw a line from the index point to the 60° mark. This angle is a 240° angle.

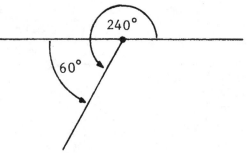

You will note that two different angle magnitudes were included. The 240° angle is made up of a 180° angle and a 60° angle.

Sometimes an angle is already drawn and your task is to construct an angle exactly like the one drawn.

Of course, you could use a protractor, measure the given angle, and then proceed as in the previous paragraph to draw the angle.

However, another procedure involves the use of a compass.

The procedure is best demonstrated in the following six steps.

Step 1.   You are given angle *XOY*. Draw base line $\overline{O'Y'}$ to the side of the given angle *XOY*.

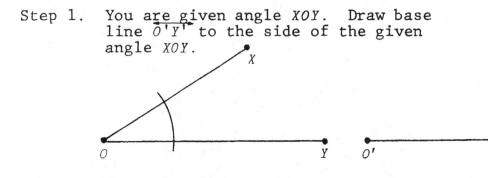

Step 2. With the compass at *O*, make an arc of any convenient length that cuts the sides $\overline{OX}$ and $\overline{OY}$ as shown. Call these points *P* and *Q*.

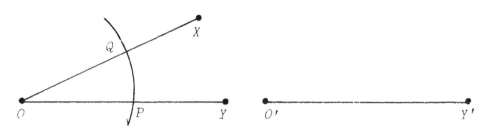

Step 3. With the compass set at the same distance, move it to *O'* and draw another arc as shown. Call this point *P'*.

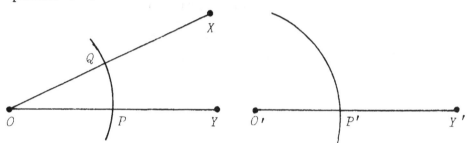

Step 4. Measure the distance along the arc from point *P* to point *Q* with your compass set at point *P*. Where the arc cuts line $\overleftrightarrow{OX}$ at point *Q* draw another arc that intersects the arc and line $\overleftrightarrow{OX}$.

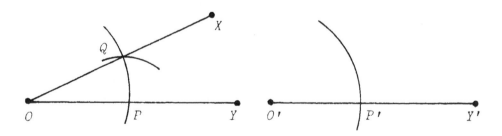

Step 5. With this same distance, move the compass to point *P'* on line $\overleftrightarrow{O'Y'}$ and make an arc to intersect the previous arc at point *Q'*.

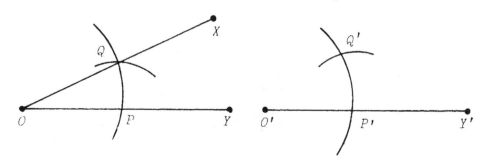

Step 6. With a straightedge, connect point *O'*
        with *Q'*.

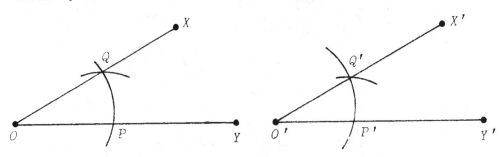

        The drawn angle is the same size as
        the given angle.

        A *perpendicular* is the shortest line that
can be drawn to a straight line from an
external point. A perpendicular intersects
the original line at right angles. Assume we
have line *AB* given as shown and a point *P*
that is external to line *AB*.

                        • *P*

Step 1. With the compass at point *P* as the center,
        and opened wide enough to cut line *AB*,
        draw the arc *A'B'* cutting *AB* at points
        A' and *B'* as shown.

                    • *P*

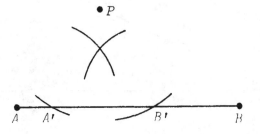

Step 2. With the compass at *A'* first and *B'*
        second with the compass opened wider than
        one half of the length of *A'B'*, draw
        two arcs intersecting at *P'* as shown.

                    • *P*

Step 3.   Now draw a line through points P and P'
          meeting $\overline{AB}$ at point O as shown.

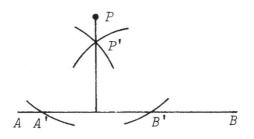

     The line just drawn is perpendicular to
line AB.   The angle POB is, by definition, a
right angle.   Angle POA is also a right
angle.   You may confirm this fact by
measuring the angles with your protractor.

■■■   Perform the following activities.

2.1   Given angle AOB, draw an angle of the same size with the
      given base line.

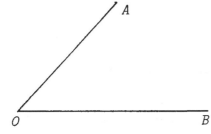

2.2   Draw a line perpendicular to the given line PP'.

          P   P'

2.3   Using a protractor, draw an angle of 80°.

          O   A

27

2.4   Draw an angle of 310° using a protractor.

```
    _____
    O                                        A
```

Teacher check _____
                    Initial   Date

███████   Write *true* or *false*.

2.5   _____ The angle 130° measured counterclockwise from
                  the right side of a base line and the angle 50°
                  measured clockwise from the right side of the
                  base line are the same angle.

2.6   _____ The three types of angles are acute, right, and
                  obtuse.

2.7   _____ A standard protractor is marked off into 270°.

2.8   _____ Drawing a perpendicular to a line forms two
                  right angles where the perpendicular and the
                  line meet.

███████   Complete the following sentences.

2.9   An angle greater than 90° is called a(n) _____.

2.10   A line dropped from an external point to meet another

        line to form right angles is called a _____.

2.11   Draftsmen normally use a _____ to draw and
        measure angles.

2.12   The perpendicular is the _____ that can be
        drawn to a straight line from an external point.

The importance of polygon construction with respect to shop drawings has already been mentioned. A polygon is a closed plane figure with any number of straight sides. Polygons are found in art, industry, and science.

Polygons derive their names from the number of sides they have. A few polygons are the triangle, the pentagon, the octagon, and the decagon. The triangle has three sides. The pentagon has five sides. The octagon has eight sides. The decagon has ten sides.

A polygon with all sides of equal length is called an *equilateral polygon*. A polygon with all its angles equal is called an *equiangluar polygon*. A polygon can be equilateral and not equiangular and vice versa, except in the case of a triangle. If a triangle is equilateral it is also equiangular, and vice versa.

A polygon that is both equilateral and equiangular is called a *regular polygon*. The vertex of an angle formed by two adjacent sides of a polygon is a vertex of the polygon. The angle inside the polygon formed by two sides of a vertex is an *interior angle*. The angle formed outside the polygon by extending one side through a vertex is an *exterior angle*.

Model: Name an interior angle and an exterior angle in the polygon shown.

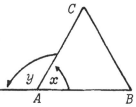

In polygon *ABC*, ∠*x* is the interior angle and ∠*y* is the exterior angle. Both angles have point *A* as their vertex.

Our selection of an equilateral triangle to demonstrate the interior and exterior angles was done purposely although we usually think of polygons as having at least five sides. Regular polygons may be thought of as making equal triangles. Thus, a regular pentagon is made up of five equilateral triangles, a regular hexagon is made up of six equilateral triangles, and so on.

Model: Show that a regular hexagon is
          made up of six equilateral triangles.

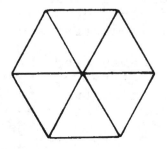

Since each equilateral triangle is also
equiangular, the interior angles of each
triangle contain 60° each (180° ÷ 3). The
hexagon has twelve interior angles around
it at the bases of the triangles. The sum
of these angles, therefore, is 12 x 60° = 720°.

This example leads us to a fundamental
rule about polygons: The sum of the interior
angles of a polygon of n sides is
$(n - 2)$ x 180°. For the hexagon, therefore,
the sum of the interior angles =
$(6 - 2)$ x 180° = 4 x 180° = 720°.

A corollary of the polygon rule is that

each interior angle of a regular polygon of

n sides is $(1 - \frac{2}{n})$ x 180°. In the regular

hexagon each interior angle =

$(1 - \frac{2}{6})$ x 180° = $\frac{2}{3}$ x 180° = 120°.

Another fact about polygons becomes
evident when we re-examine the hexagon
drawn in the model. The area of the
hexagon appears to be composed of the sum
of the six equilateral triangles that
were drawn inside the hexagon.

Let us examine one of these triangles.

The length of each of its sides as drawn

in the following figure is $\frac{2}{3}$". We know that

the area of a triangle is equal to half

the product of its base times its altitude.

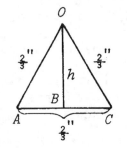

30

By dropping a perpendicular to the base, we form a right triangle OBA as shown. AB is one half of base AC, and so is equal to $\frac{1}{3}$". From the Pythagorean Theorem we know that $h^2 = \left(\frac{2}{3}\right)^2 - \left(\frac{1}{3}\right)^2$, or $h^2 = \frac{4}{9} - \frac{1}{9} = \frac{3}{9} = \frac{1}{3}$. Therefore, $h = \sqrt{\frac{1}{3}} = \frac{\sqrt{3}}{3}$.

The area of triangle OAC then, is equal to $\frac{1}{2} \times \frac{2}{3} \times \frac{\sqrt{3}}{3}$. Multiplying, we obtain the area $A = \frac{\sqrt{3}}{9}$ = 0.1924444 in.^{2}. Since a hexagon has six of these triangles, the hexagon's area = 6(0.1924444) = 1.155 in.^{2}.

Fortunately, we do not have to go through all these steps to compute the areas of various polygons. A table has been prepared that expresses the area of each of the more common regular polygons as a function of the length of one of its sides.

Number of Sides	Name	Area
3	Equilateral triangle	$0.433s^2$
4	Square	$1.000s^2$
5	Pentagon	$1.720s^2$
6	Hexagon	$2.598s^2$
7	Heptagon	$3.634s^2$
8	Octagon	$4.828s^2$
9	Nonagon	$6.182s^2$
10	Decagon	$7.694s^2$

Model: Check the area of the hexagon that was computed the long way previously by using the table furnished.

$$s = \frac{2}{3}"$$
$$A = 2.598\left(\frac{2}{3}\right)^2$$
$$A = 2.598\left(\frac{4}{9}\right)$$
$$A = 1.155 \text{ in.}^2$$

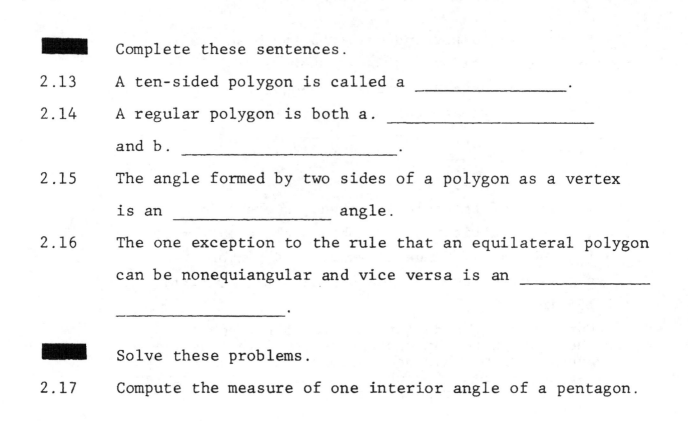

Complete these sentences.

2.13   A ten-sided polygon is called a _____.

2.14   A regular polygon is both a. _____

        and b. _____.

2.15   The angle formed by two sides of a polygon as a vertex

        is an _____ angle.

2.16   The one exception to the rule that an equilateral polygon

        can be nonequiangular and vice versa is an _____

        _____.

Solve these problems.

2.17   Compute the measure of one interior angle of a pentagon.

2.18   Compute the measure of one interior angle of a dodecagon
        (12-sided polygon).

2.19   Find the sum of the interior angles of a heptagon.

32

CONSUMER MATHEMATICS 9

LIFEPAC TEST

50 / 62

Name _____

Date _____

Score _____

CONSUMER MATHEMATICS 9: LIFEPAC TEST

Match these items (each answer, 2 points).

1. _____ representation of an object in three dimensions

2. _____ number below the line in a fraction

3. _____ an angle with fewer degrees than a right angle

4. _____ polygon with six sides

5. _____ an angle of 111°

6. _____ has an interior angle of 108°

7. _____ instrument for copying angles

8. _____ instrument for measuring angles

a. denominator

b. perspective

c. acute

d. pentagon

e. protractor

f. compass

g. obtuse

h. hexagon

i. numerator

Write the correct letter in the space provided (each answer, 2 points).

9. A six-digit number in the grid coordinate system will locate an object on a map to the _____.

   a. nearest 10,000 square meters   c. nearest 100 square meters

   b. nearest square kilometer   d. nearest 10,000 square kilometers

10. Contour lines closely spaced together denote a _____.

   a. valley   c. gradual slope

   b. mountain top   d. steep slope

11. The index point of a protractor is placed on an angle so that the index point is directly over the angle's _____.

   a. vertex   b. hypotenuse   c. grid   d. side

Write *true* or *false* (each answer, 2 points).

12. _____ The cutouts used for floor and room plans are called templates.

13. _____ A regular dodecagon cannot be inscribed in a circle.

14. _____ Competition within the carpeting industry is one reason for the wide range of prices in carpeting.

15. _____ An architect typically employs a scale of $\frac{1}{2}'' = 6'$ when drawing a house plan.

16. _____ A given contour line indicates the same elevation above sea level all along its arc.

Complete the following items (each answer, 3 points).

17. Compute the value of C in the expression $C:16::6:8$.

_____

18. Add $\frac{1}{8}$, $\frac{2}{24}$, $\frac{5}{12}$, and $\frac{3}{8}$.   _____

19. Copy the following angle using a compass and straightedge.

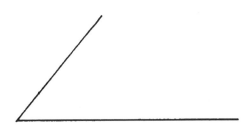

20. Based on the table of areas of regular polygons at the end of this LIFEPAC, compute the area of a regular heptagon with a side of 4" (answer to the nearest whole number).

_____

2

21. Calculate the total floor area of the following house plan.

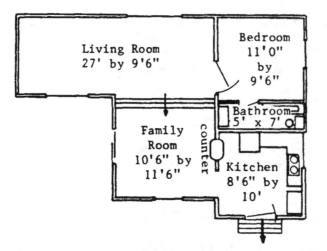

22. Work this problem based on the dimensions shown in Problem 21 and on the table showing costs of furnishings at the end of this LIFEPAC. Assume you are going to lay cork tile in the family room, vinyl in the kitchen, and nylon carpeting in the living room and bedroom. How much will the cost be to cover each of these floors and what will the total cost be, assuming you buy the least expensive covering?

    a. Family room   _____

    b. Kitchen   _____

    c. Living room   _____

    d. Bedroom   _____

    e. Total cost   _____

2.20   Find the sum of the interior angles of a decagon.

2.21   Compute the area of a regular hexagon with each side equal to 2".

2.22   Compute the area of a regular nonagon with each side equal to 5".

◄◄◄ INSCRIBING REGULAR POLYGONS ►►►►►►►►►►►►►►►►►►►►

Of particular interest to draftsmen is inscribing regular polygons in circles. Not only does the technique use a number of geometric principles, but it also leads to a very practical method of measuring the circle.

The technique used to inscribe a square in a circle is rather simple. Let *O* be the center of a circle. Through *O* draw a line (diameter of the circle). Then construct a perpendicular diameter to that line as shown.

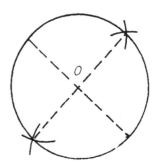

Next, connect the end points to form
a square, square *ABCD*.

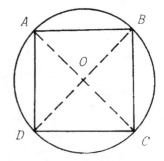

If we were to double the number of sides
of the inscribed square we would obtain an
octagon, octagon *ABCDEFGH*.

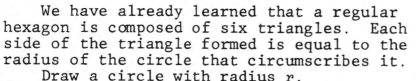

We have already learned that a regular
hexagon is composed of six triangles. Each
side of the triangle formed is equal to the
radius of the circle that circumscribes it.
    Draw a circle with radius *r*.

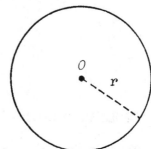

Now mark off on the circle's circumference
distances equal to this radius; you will have
six such marks. When these marks are connected,
they will form a hexagon.

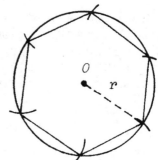

We can also inscribe an equilateral triangle by connecting every other mark or corner of an inscribed regular hexagon. We can obtain an inscribed regular dodecagon (twelve-sided polygon) by doubling the number of sides of the inscribed regular hexagon.

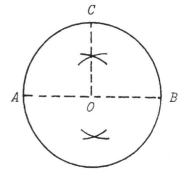

The procedure for inscribing a regular pentagon is slightly more complicated than the procedures for inscribing squares, octagons, hexagons, and triangles. In a given circle draw a diameter, and at the center of the diameter, erect a perpendicular.

Next, bisect radius *OA* into *AD* and *DO*. Using *D* as the center of *AO*, and with a radius equal to *DC*, mark off *DE* equal to *DC*.

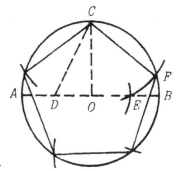

Next, with center at *C* and radius of the length of *CE*, draw an arc *EF* that intersects the circle at *F*. Draw the line *CF*, which is one side of the pentagon. Marking the length of *CF* five times around the circumference of the circle gives us the connecting points for the inscribed pentagon.

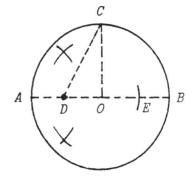

Note: The construction method for the hexagon and pentagon may not produce precisely regular polygons.

▮▮▮ Complete these activities.

2.23 Given this circle, inscribe an equilateral triangle.

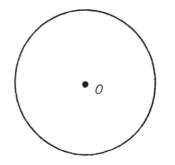

2.24   Given this circle, inscribe a regular decagon.

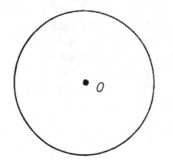

    Match these items.

2.25   _____ polygon side equals radius   a. nonagon

2.26   _____ nine-sided polygon   b. $(1 - \frac{2}{n})180°$

2.27   _____ sum of interior angles   c. hexagon

2.28   _____ each interior angle   d. dodecagon

2.29   _____ twelve-sided polygon   e. $(n - 2)180°$

                                                 f. heptagon

Teacher check _____
                    Initial   Date

Review the material in this section in preparation for the Self Test. This Self Test will check your mastery of this particular section as well as your knowledge of the previous section.

SELF TEST 2

Write *true* or *false* (each answer, 2 points).

2.01   _____ The number $\frac{6}{3}$ is a fraction.

2.02   _____ To reduce $\frac{9}{27}$ divide both numbers by 9.

2.03   _____ The second and third terms in a proportion are called the means.

2.04   _____ The figure 1:20,000 on a map is called a converted fraction.

2.05   _____ A map scale may be represented by a graphic line scale.

Select the correct choice (each answer, 2 points).

2.06   Polygons derive their names from _____.

    a. the number of sides
    b. the magnitude of the interior angles
    c. the technique for inscription
    d. the total number of degrees

2.07   The simplest method to inscribe an equilateral triangle

is to _____.

    a. bisect the interior angles of a square
    b. work off the circumference of the circle into thirds
    c. inscribe a hexagon first
    d. make the circle's diameter the length of the triangle's sides

2.08   The perpendicular to a line _____.

    a. bisects the line
    b. meets the line at right angles
    c. forms an obtuse angle with the line
    d. forms a square

2.09   A compass _____.

    a. contains 180°
    b. is used to mark arcs
    c. cannot be used to erect perpendiculars
    d. is used only for constructing circles

2.010   Map scales were developed to _____.

    a. convert distances between points anywhere in the world to the same map distance
    b. show how one map compares to another map
    c. weigh maps
    d. reduce actual distances to manageable distances

Match the correct items (each answer, 2 points).

2.011 _____ angle less than 90°

2.012 _____ angle greater than
               180° but less than
               360°

2.013 _____ closed plane figure

2.014 _____ angle greater than 90°

2.015 _____ angle formed at vertex
               of polygon

a. constructed by inverting
   protractor

b. obtuse angle

c. acute angle

d. interior angle

e. exterior angle

f. polygon

Solve the following problems (each answer, 3 points).

2.016 Given $C:3 = 96:36$; solve for C. _____

2.017 Given a map scale of 1:75,000, what is the ground
       distance in nearest whole miles between two mines that
       are 7.5 inches apart on the map?

                                          _____

2.018 If the sides of a regular heptagon are 2.5 inches
       each, what is the heptagon's area? (Answer to the
       nearest tenth of an inch.)

                                          _____

2.019 Determine the sum of the interior angles of
       an octagon.

                                          _____

2.020 We know that an octagon has twice as many sides as a
       square. Is the sum of the interior angles of a square
       half the sum of the interior angles of an octagon?

                                          _____

Perform the following activities (each activity, 4 points).

2.021 Inscribe an equiangular triangle in the circle given.

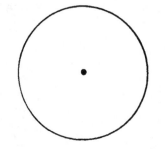

2.022 Use the formula to compute the measure of each interior
       angle of a pentagon; then draw and label one such angle
       using a protractor.

2.023 Demonstrate that perpendiculars drawn from the midpoints
       of each side of the given rectangle all meet at a common
       point.

2.024 Based on the given contour representation, construct a
       side view of the mountain.

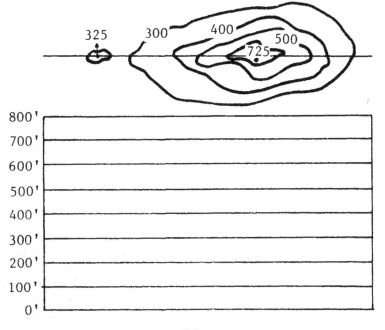

2.025   Copy the following angle by using a compass but not
         a protractor.

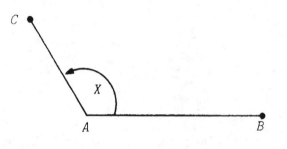

III. HOUSE PLANS

OBJECTIVES

9. To answer questions about scaled diagrams used in house plans.

10. To answer questions about floor plans including placement of furnishings.

11. To calculate costs associated with furnishing a house.

Custom-built homes have always been unique in their design to reflect the owner's life style, tastes, and personality. Tract houses (a group of identical houses, such as houses in subdivisions, that are on lots of equal size) have undergone the most dramatic evolution, particularly since the days of World War II. The so-called victory houses that were built *en masse* right after World War II have also undergone much change.

House plans have come to feature comfort and convenience. Technological innovations in building materials, in construction techniques, and in methods of fabrication have also allowed the architect and interior decorator to exercise much greater flexibility and originality than they would have been able to exercise thirty-five years ago.

DIAGRAMMING HOUSE PLANS

A house plan should be diagrammed so that each room is a vital component of the total plan. Therefore, each room should reflect the primary function and the predominant activities that will take place in it.

Since costs are related to the square footage of construction contained in a house, the planner should endeavor to utilize as much space as possible for living space. He should also try to keep the design simple to hold down costs. A third consideration, and a very important one, is family privacy.

Any particular room has no "best size."
Some general guidelines, however, provide
the planner with a range of room sizes.
These room sizes are based upon the normal
activities that take place in the rooms;
the size of the family; the general age
group of the house dwellers; and the kinds
of furniture, appliances, and possessions
such families are likely to have.

The following table shows the respective
room-size ranges for different types of
families.

ROOM-SIZE RANGE

ROOM	RETIREMENT FAMILY or BEGINNING FAMILY	FOUR-MEMBER FAMILY	FAMILY WITH THREE TEEN-AGERS	FAMILY WITH FIVE CHILDREN
Kitchen	50-80 ft.^{2}	84-96 ft.^{2}	108-154 ft.^{2}	154-172 ft.^{2}
Dining Room	90-110 ft.^{2}	100-117 ft.^{2}	117-140 ft.^{2}	140-160 ft.^{2}
Dinette	25-30 ft.^{2}	30-48 ft.^{2}	56-64 ft.^{2}	64-78 ft.^{2}
Living Room	140-170 ft.^{2}	174-219 ft.^{2}	238-262 ft.^{2}	262-300 ft.^{2}
Master Bedroom	120-134 ft.^{2}	120-134 ft.^{2}	134-172 ft.^{2}	134-172 ft.^{2}
Bathroom	35-48 ft.^{2}	35-48 ft.^{2}	40-54 ft.^{2}	48-54 ft.^{2}
Second Bedroom or Den	90-110 ft.^{2}	100-120 ft.^{2}	100-120 ft.^{2}	100-120 ft.^{2}
Family Room		154 ft.^{2}	192-216 ft.^{2}	216-273 ft.^{2}
Bathroom	35 ft.^{2}	35-40 ft.^{2}	1: 40-44 ft.$\frac{1}{2}$: 30 ft.	2: 40-44 ft.^{2} $\frac{1}{2}$: 35 ft.^{2}
Carport	193 ft.^{2}	218 ft.^{2}		
Two-Car Garage			333 ft.^{2}	410 ft.^{2}
TOTAL SPACE	778-910 ft.^{2}	1,050-1,194 ft.^{2}	1,388-1,589 ft.^{2}	1,603-1,858 ft.^{2}

Notice the wide range in total square feet for the retirement or beginning family space. This range is to allow for the considerable variation of space for retirement couples, since they may be living on a fixed income. Also, note that even though only one more family member has been added to the next category after the four-member family, allowances were made in the ranges because the children are all teen-agers who require more space (one bedroom each and a much larger dining room, living room, and family room).

Model 1: What are the percentage increases in the ranges of total space for the retirement family and for the family with three teen-agers respectively?

Percentage increase for retirement family
$$= \frac{910 - 778}{778} = \frac{132}{778} = 17\%.$$

Percentage increase for family with three teen-agers $= \frac{1,829 - 1,588}{1,588} = \frac{241}{1,588} = 15\%.$

Model 2: Referring to the smallest master bedroom and the largest master bedroom listed in the table, note that their sizes range from 120 square feet to 172 square feet. What might the room sizes be (select two appropriate sizes each)?

The smallest master bedroom is 120 ft.^{2}. The square root of 120 ft.^{2} is approximately 11 ft. Therefore, for the smaller bedroom the size could be 10'0" x 12'0" or 10'8" x 11'3". Both dimensions produce 120 ft.^{2} of space.

The largest bedroom is 172 ft.^{2}. The square root of 172 ft.^{2} is just a little more than 13 ft. Therefore, the largest bedroom could be 12'0" x 14'4" or 10'9" x 16'0".

Other combinations will, of course, produce the required square footage, but consideration must be given to keeping the room's dimensions fairly close (in length and in width). Also avoid perfect squares as much as you can so that long furniture, such as beds and sofas, can be placed to allow for movement, access, and room for other furniture.

Once room sizes have been decided upon, the important task of room placement must be tackled. Certain room combinations are fairly obvious. The dining room should be next to the kitchen. If you have a family room it should be adjacent to the kitchen, since families use this room for informal snacks, get-togethers, and other activities. The front entrance is usually located near the living room, and the back entrance is usually located off the kitchen and/or the family room. The sleeping area is generally set off by itself at one end of the house or is upstairs for privacy. Quite naturally, the bathrooms should be located for easy access from the bedrooms, except that a guest bathroom might be more centrally located, or located off the family room.

Outside of these general guidelines, all sorts of possibilities exist for room placement and are dependent on a number of factors. One of these factors is the orientation of the lot. For example, the rising and the setting of the sun should be considered. Usually, a family wants the morning sun's warmth for the living areas, and the afternoon shade for the living areas. To achieve this setting means orienting these areas to face south. The kitchen will then face either to the north, the east, or the northeast.

The emphasis on outdoor living in certain areas of the country sometimes suggests shifting the living areas. For example, the living areas could face north where the backyard patio is located. The living areas can be protected somewhat with overhangs, screenings, and terraces.

Another factor sometimes overlooked is
the need for future expansion as family needs
change. Flexibility is the keynote. Perhaps
the desired modifications can be achieved
by converting the garage into a family room,
or by adding a dormer (an upright window
built out from a sloping roof) to an
unfinished attic to allow more headroom, or
by converting the basement space to extra
bedroom and bathroom facilities.

Templates, or room cutouts, are an
excellent technique for making floor plans
of houses. The technique generally
involves the following steps:

Step 1.   Sketch the rooms on coordinate graph
          paper prelined to a scale of $\frac{1}{4}$ inch =
          1 foot or $\frac{1}{8}$ inch = 1 foot. Label
          the rooms and cut them out.

Step 2.   On another sheet of graph paper, draw
          the boundaries of the house lot. Use
          the same scale as with the rooms. On
          this sheet, sketch important
          topographical features such as streets,
          utility poles, and North.

Step 3.   Arrange the room templates on the lot
          sketch in combinations that generally
          follow the previous guidelines.

Step 4.   Try to find the best arrangement by
          considering such things as ease of
          service circulation, traffic (indoor)
          circulation, diversity of family
          activities, economy, and full potential
          for each room with regard to its
          livability.

Step 5.   Once the preferred arrangement has
          been found, separate the rooms by
          about 6" (in scale) for interior walls
          and about 10" for exterior walls. Allow
          for stairwells, closets, hallways, and
          storage space.

Step 6.   Locate the windows and doors with
          consideration for views, traffic
          circulation, ease of furniture
          placement, and privacy.

This list is not meant to be all-inclusive. It is only a suggestion of some of the more elemental considerations to be factored into room placement.

Model 1: Critique the following tentative bedroom and bathroom placement.

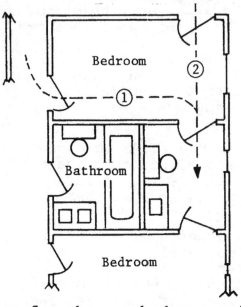

The proposed plan for the top bedroom and its half bathroom is poor because of the placement of the doors. As the rooms are situated now, traffic circulates either along Route 1 or along Route 2 to use the bathroom. This situation makes furniture placement along two walls impossible. Generally, rooms should be kept free of traffic lanes such as these.

Model 2: Critique the following door placement.

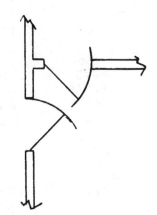

The doors actually conflict with each other as they are currently placed. They open toward each other, which could cause possible accidents or at least cause door collisions.

Write *true* or *false*.

3.1 _____ As life styles have changed since the 1950's, privacy is no longer an important consideration in house design.

3.2 _____ A family with teen-agers should look for larger floor plans than a family with young children because of increased space needs for teen-age living and activities.

3.3 _____ Because of the simplicity of constructing square rooms, architects try to plan rooms in square shapes.

3.4 _____ Additional rooms may be provided by expansion and conversion.

3.5 _____ A good rule to follow in providing for traffic circulation is to keep rooms free of traffic lanes.

Perform the following calculations.

3.6 What is the average space suggested per person in a 7-member family, based on the table previously provided?

3.7 How much space is suggested as an average per individual in a five-member family, three of whom are teen-agers?

3.8 The minimum full bathroom size recommended contains how many square feet?

3.9 Given a retirement couple or beginning family, what would be the average dimensions of a kitchen as recommended by the table? (answer in length and width)

■ Perform the following activities.

3.10 List at least three considerations when determining room size.

a. _____

_____

b. _____

_____

c. _____

_____

3.11 List the considerations when trying out various room combinations on graph paper with room templates.

_____

_____

_____

_____

_____

_____

✓ Teacher check_____
                        Initial   Date

∿∿∿∿∿∿ FURNISHINGS ∿∿∿∿∿∿∿∿∿∿∿∿∿∿∿∿

All you need to do to realize the importance of furnishings in making a house salable is to visit the model homes at a construction site. Professional interior decorators are able to transform even the plainest house into an attractive and appealing one. This appeal is achieved through the judicious and artistic blend of color, form, scale, and accents. Many houses have been sold on the basis of the manner in which they were furnished and decorated to accentuate their positive features and to minimize their negative features.

Most newly built and resold houses now have carpeting throughout the living areas. The living areas are the bedrooms, the living room, the dining room, and the connecting hallways. The family room may have carpeting. Some family rooms utilize a form of indoor-outdoor carpeting that can withstand much hard use.

The way to figure the cost of carpeting
is to measure the rooms and the areas to be
covered. Add the square footages obtained
for all these rooms and divide this number
by 9 to convert it to square yards. Carpeting
is sold by the square yard and varies con-
siderably in the ranges of quality, durability,
and type (shag, looped, sculptured, or velvet),
due to competition in the industry.

Shop around before you select your carpet,
as with any purchase. What may sound like
a good buy in terms of cost may prove not
to be such a wise choice if after the carpet
is installed, you discover that it detracts
from the other furnishings or that it is
shoddy in appearance.

Another thing to be particularly alert
to in your carpet shopping is the quality
of padding included in the price of installation. Many so-called bargains become less
so because the padding underneath the carpet
is too thin and too cheaply constructed.

Model 1: Rooms to be carpeted:
living room 18'0" by 12'6";
1 bedroom 11'0" by 10'6";
2 bedrooms 10'6" by 10'0" each; and
hallway 21'0" by 4'6".
Cost of carpeting with padding
and installation $9.95 per
square yard.

Find the cost of carpeting required.

Room areas: 225   ft.^{2}
              115.5
              210
               94.5
              645.0 ft.^{2}

645 ÷ 9 = 71.67 yd.^{2}

Cost = 71.67 x $9.95 = $713.12,
tax not included.

Model 2: Before signing the purchase order for the
carpet and padding in the previous
problem, you decide that you like the
carpeting, but that you would like a
heavier padding. You find that
heavier padding costs an additional
$1.25 per sq. yd. How much is the
total cost now?

Cost = 71.67 x ($9.95 + $1.25)
= 71.67 x $11.20 = $802.70.

Furniture placement is handled by the same technique as room placement. *Templates* of the various furniture pieces are prepared. Figure 7 shows some of the more representative pieces with some of the more popular sizes.

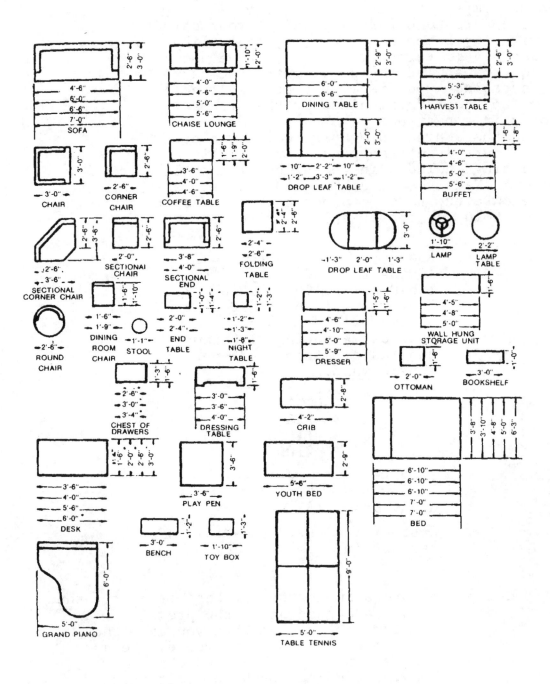

Figure 7: Furniture Templates

A sheet of graph paper is marked according to the dimensions of the room being studied and the scale selected.

The appropriate furniture is then placed in the room to conform to window, door, and closet locations and to proper clearances (distances between pieces of furniture). For example, for the living room the recommended minimum clearances are as shown in Figure 8.

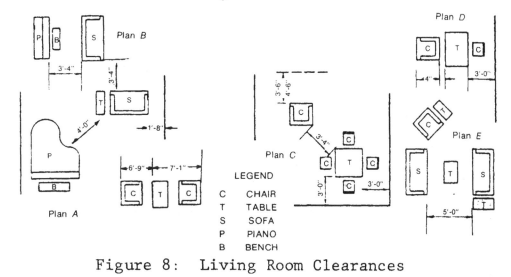

Figure 8: Living Room Clearances

The bedroom has one critical dimension, the clearance around the bed. At least twenty inches should be provided on both sides of the bed and at the foot of the bed.

An important dimension in the kitchen is the "work triangle," shown in Figure 9.

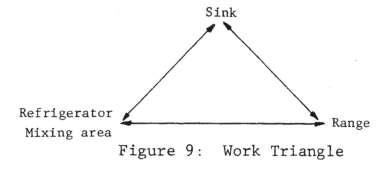

Figure 9: Work Triangle

The work triangle should have a perimeter of about seventeen feet.

■■■■ Match these items.

3.12 _____ template   a. 20"

3.13 _____ graph paper   b. 17'

3.14 _____ minimium clearance c. pattern
           around bed
                               d. room dimensions are
3.15 _____ perimeter of work   drawn on it
           triangle
                               e. 24"

■■■■ Select the appropriate letter to complete each
     statement.

3.16 In figuring the cost of carpeting a room, divide the

     square footage of the room by _____

     a. 12   b. 3   c. 9   d. 6

3.17 Before placing furniture in a room, you need to consider

     _____.

     a. window, door, and closet locations

     b. color and type of wall covering

     c. number of electrical outlets

     d. types of curtains in the room

3.18 In planning the kitchen, you should keep in mind _____.

     a. the food to be prepared

     b. the number of cabinets

     c. the location of the refrigerator

     d. the work triangle

▼▼▼▼▼ **COST-SAVING GUIDELINES** ▼▼▼▼▼▼▼▼▼▼▼▼▼▼▼▼

    Even with high inflation the person
furnishing his home can achieve
modernization at a reasonable cost in a
number of ways.
    You add character to a room by avoiding
monotony in color. Mixing colors and styles
can create varying moods in a room thereby
maintaining the room's uniqueness.
    Wallpaper has recently become popular
again because with modern adhesives, you

no longer need to have a professional paper hanger to do a good job. Also, the number of designs and color patterns has greatly increased the opportunity to find just the right touch you might be looking for. No longer do you need to cover all the walls with the same pattern or color of wallpaper; one covered wall both achieves focal interest and adds dimension to a room.

Some people place mirrored tile on a wall to add beauty and depth, particularly in the dining room. A mural also adds interest to an otherwise drab interior.

Many good buys may be found in purchasing odd-sized carpets or rugs, which are otherwise in good condition. Watch the newspapers for furniture sales. Many stores will cut the prices of their floor samples drastically when a shipment of new carpet arrives. If a piece of carpet is marked "As Is," be sure to inspect it thoroughly because the warning "As Is" lets you know that the carpet has some defect or damage.

As with many other goods, furniture is a seasonal commodity. The alert shopper can save as much as 50 per cent during special sales periodically offered by furniture and furnishing stores.

Picking up and transporting your purchase may also save you money, since the cost of loading and transporting is normally added on to the price of the merchandise.

A representative list has been prepared of some standard furnishings to give you an idea of the wide range in costs per item and to give you practice in cost estimation for decorating a home.

The prices in this list have been selected to provide practice in computing costs. It is likely that they will not reflect current pricing or availability.

Item	Cost
Floor coverings, hard	Per sq. yd., installed
Cork	$5.00 - $10.50
Vinyl	2.60 - 15.00
Linoleum	3.45 - 6.00
Floor coverings, soft	
Acrilan	$8.00 - $22.50
Nylon	5.50 - 45.00
Rayon	4.00 - 22.00

Padding

Hair and jute	$1.10 -	$3.00
Sponge rubber	1.75 -	6.00

Wall coverings	Per sq. yd., not installed	
Grass cloth	$4.00 -	$7.50
Paint	0.50 -	0.30
Wallpaper	0.05 -	3.00

Window treatments

Venetian blinds	$3.45 -	$22.00
Cotton curtains	2.00 -	15.00
Fiberglass curtains	2.30 -	18.75
Rayon and acetate curtains	2.30 -	11.25

Furniture

Studio couch	$ 45.00 -	$ 500.00
Sofa	115.00 -	1,000.00
Chair, padded	15.00 -	150.00
Chair, upholstered	35.00 -	450.00
Table, dining	45.00 -	600.00
Table, coffee and end	9.00 -	225.00
Bed, foam rubber mattress and box springs	50.00 -	525.00
Bed, innerspring mattress and box springs	55.00 -	150.00
metal frame with casters	8.00 -	30.00
headboard	9.45 -	300.00
Lamp, floor	11.50 -	225.00
Lamp, table	6.90 -	150.00
Washer	238.00 -	318.00
Dryer	220.00 -	285.00
Refrigerator	300.00 -	530.00
Microwave oven	180.00 -	350.00
Air conditioner	170.00 -	450.00

Model 1: You are furnishing your living room
with a sofa, two upholstered chairs,
a coffee table, two end tables, and
two table lamps. What is the range
of total costs for these items on the
table provided?

	Low Cost	High Cost
Sofa	$115.00	$1,000.00
Chair (2)	70.00	900.00
Table (3)	27.00	675.00
Lamp (2)	13.80	300.00
Total Cost	$225.80	$2,875.00

Model 2: Your kitchen is 72 ft.^{2}, your family
room is 154 ft.^{2}, and your living room
is 180 ft.^{2}. Based upon the cost
table provided, calculate the total
cost to lay lineoleum on your kitchen
floor, vinyl on your family-room floor,
and nylon carpeting with hair and jute
padding on your living-room floor.
Assume you purchase the items at the
lowest prices listed.

Cost of linoleum for kitchen:
$$\frac{72}{9} = 8 \text{ yd.}^2$$
8 x $3.45 = $27.60

Cost of vinyl for family room:
$$\frac{154}{9} = 17.11 \text{ yd.}^2$$
17.11 x $2.60 = $44.49

Cost of nylon carpet for living room:
$$\frac{180}{9} = 20 \text{ yd.}^2$$
20 x $5.50 = $110.00

Cost of hair and jute padding:
20 x $1.10 = $22.00

Total cost
= $27.60 + $44.49 + $110.00 + $22.00
= $204.09

■ Match these items.

3.19 _____ shag   a. type of padding

3.20 _____ hair and jute   b. type of hard floor covering

3.21 _____ vinyl   c. type of curtain

3.22 _____ fiberglass   d. type of carpet

3.23 _____ grass cloth   e. odd-sized carpet

3.24 _____ remnant   f. type of wall paper

                                    g. type of hardwood floor

■ Write *true* or *false*.

3.25 _____ If you buy a plush carpet, you need not concern
              yourself with the quality of padding.

3.26 _____ Discounts on furnishings should be avoided since
              they are generally associated with shabby
              merchandise.

3.27 _____ One major consideration of furniture placement
              is traffic circulation.

3.28 _____ Templates of furniture are beneficial devices for
              trying out various room arrangements.

✓ Teacher check_____
                      Initial   Date

 Before you take this last Self Test, you may want to do one or more of
these self checks.

1. ____ Read the objectives. Determine if you can do them.

2. ____ Restudy the material related to any objectives that you cannot do.

3. ____ Use the SQ3R study procedure to review the material:
   a. **S**can the sections,
   b. **Q**uestion yourself again (review the questions you wrote
      initially),
   c. **R**ead to answer your questions,
   d. **R**ecite the answers to yourself, and
   e. **R**eview areas you didn't understand.

4. ____ Review all activities, and Self Tests, writing a correct answer for
   each wrong answer.

SELF TEST 3

List six different kinds of floor covering material (each answer, 2 points).

3.01 _____   3.04 _____

3.02 _____   3.05 _____

3.03 _____   3.06 _____

Complete the following sentences (each answer, 3 points).

3.07   Besides using a template, one should prepare _____

_____ on which a room's dimensions are drawn to

scale.

3.08   A typical protractor includes a semicircle marked off in

degrees from 0° to 180° and an _____.

3.09   When someone wishes to add or subtract fractions, he

should change all denominators to the _____.

3.010   A method of stating the relationship between two numbers

is the calculation of the _____.

3.011   A proportion is a statement of _____.

3.012   Lines showing elevations are called _____.

3.013   The measurement of the outside border of a field is

called its _____.

3.014   The size of a plan, a map, a drawing, or a model compared

with what it represents is a _____.

Given the following grid, locate the park (this answer, 3 points).

3.015   Park location: _____

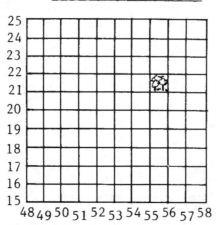

Work the following problems (each problem, 3 points).

3.016   Write the formula for computing the area of a triangle.

_____

3.017   List the three types of angles. Construct and label
an example of each kind.

a. _____

b. _____

c. _____

3.018   Construct a perpendicular to the line shown by using
a compass.

_____

3.019 Use the table showing areas of polygons at the end of this LIFEPAC to compute the area of a regular nonagon with a side of 2⅓" (answer to the nearest tenth of an inch).

_____

3.020 Compute the number of square yards in a room measuring 10'6" by 11'9" (answer to the nearest tenth of a yard).

_____

3.021 Draw an angle of 80° using a protractor.

3.022 Inscribe a regular hexagon in the circle provided.

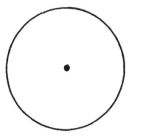

3.023 Based on the table showing costs of furnishings at the end of this LIFEPAC, calculate the percentage differences for the following prices (each part, 4 points).

a. Lowest price and highest price of hard floor coverings.

_____

b. Lowest price and highest price of chairs.

_____

c. Lowest price and highest price of lamps.

_____

3.024　You select the average priced acrilan carpet with an average priced sponge rubber pad with which to cover
a. a living room that measures 18'6" by 21',
b. a dining room that measures 10'6" by 9'6", and
c. a hallway that measures 25' by 4'6".   Compute the cost of carpet and padding for each room (each part, 4 points).

a. _____

b. _____

c. _____

Score　　　　_____

✓ Teacher check _____

　　　　　　　　Initial　　　Date

　Before taking the LIFEPAC Test, you may want to do one or more of these self checks.

1. _____　Read the objectives. Check to see if you can do them.
2. _____　Restudy the material related to any objective that you cannot do.
3. _____　Use the SQ3R study procedure to review the material.
4. _____　Review activities, Self Tests, and LIFEPAC Glossary.
5. _____　Restudy areas of weakness indicated by the last Self Test.

GLOSSARY

cartographer.   A maker of maps.

equiangular.   Having all angles equal.

equilateral.   Having all sides equal.

exterior angle.   The angle outside a polygon formed by extending one side through a vertex.

grid.   A system of evenly spaced lines that form a lattice as an aid to locating objects on a map.

interior angle.   The angle inside a polygon formed by the two sides at a vertex.

polygon.   A closed plane figure of any number of straight sides.

scale.   The size of a plan, a map, a drawing, or a model compared with what it represents.

template.   A model on which something is formed or based; a pattern.

TABLES

AREAS OF POLYGONS

Number of Sides	Name	Area
3	Equilateral triangle	$0.433s^2$
4	Square	$1.000s^2$
5	Pentagon	$1.720s^2$
6	Hexagon	$2.598s^2$
7	Heptagon	$3.634s^2$
8	Octagon	$4.828s^2$
9	Nonagon	$6.182s^2$
10	Decagon	$7.694s^2$

ROOM-SIZE RANGE

ROOM	RETIREMENT FAMILY or BEGINNING FAMILY	FOUR-MEMBER FAMILY	FAMILY WITH THREE TEEN-AGERS	FAMILY WITH FIVE CHILDREN
Kitchen	50–80 ft.^{2}	84–96 ft.^{2}	108–154 ft.^{2}	154–172 ft.^{2}
Dining Room	90–110 ft.^{2}	100–117 ft.^{2}	117–140 ft.^{2}	140–160 ft.^{2}
Dinette	25–30 ft.^{2}	30–48 ft.^{2}	56–64 ft.^{2}	64–78 ft.^{2}
Living Room	140–170 ft.^{2}	174–219 ft.^{2}	238–262 ft.^{2}	262–300 ft.^{2}[2]
Master Bedroom	120–134 ft.^{2}	120–134 ft.^{2}	134–172 ft.^{2}	134–172 ft.^{2}[2]
Bathroom	35–48 ft.^{2}	35–48 ft.^{2}	40–54 ft.^{2}	48–54 ft.^{2}
Second Bedroom or Den	90–110 ft.^{2}	100–120 ft.^{2}	100–120 ft.^{2}	100–120 ft.^{2}
Family Room		154 ft.^{2}	192–216 ft.^{2}	216–273 ft.^{2}
Bathroom	35 ft.^{2}	35–40 ft.^{2}	1: 40–44 ft. $\frac{1}{2}$: 30 ft.	2: 40–44 ft.^{2} $\frac{1}{2}$: 35 ft.^{2}
Carport	193 ft.^{2}	218 ft.^{2}		
Two-Car Garage			333 ft.^{2}	410 ft.^{2}
TOTAL SPACE	778–910 ft.^{2}	1,050–1,194 ft.^{2}	1,388–1,589 ft.^{2}	1,603–1,858 ft.^{2}

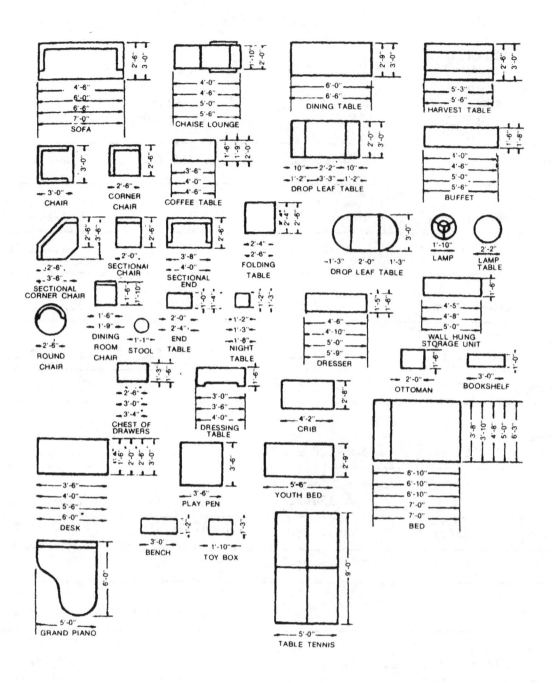

Figure 7: Furniture Templates

The prices in this list have been selected to provide practice in computing costs. It is likely that they will not reflect current pricing or availability.

COSTS OF STANDARD FURNISHINGS

Item	Cost
Floor coverings, hard	Per sq. yd., installed
Cork	$5.00 - $10.50
Vinyl	2.60 - 15.00
Linoleum	3.45 - 6.00
Floor coverings, soft	
Acrilan	$8.00 - $22.50
Nylon	5.50 - 45.00
Rayon	4.00 - 22.00
Padding	
Hair and jute	$ 1.10 - $ 3.00
Sponge rubber	1.75 - 6.00
Wall coverings	Per sq. yd., not installed
Grass cloth	$ 4.00 - $ 7.50
Paint	0.50 - 0.30
Wallpaper	0.05 - 3.00
Window treatments	
Venetian blinds	$ 3.45 - $ 22.00
Cotton curtains	2.00 - 15.00
Fiberglass curtains	2.30 - 18.75
Rayon and acetate curtains	2.30 - 11.25